D0765964

**Books are to be returned on or before
the last date stamped below.**

The Ice People
by David Orme
Illustrated by Jorge Mongiovi and Ulises Carpintero
Cover photograph: © Rudi Gobbo

Published by Ransom Publishing Ltd.
Radley House, 8 St. Cross Road, Winchester, Hampshire SO23 9HX
www.ransom.co.uk

ISBN   978 184167 453 7

First published in 2011
Reprinted 2013

Originally published in 1998 by Stanley Thornes Publishers Ltd.

A CIP catalogue record of this book is available from the British Library.

CONTENTS

NOT FOR THE PUBLIC TO KNOW

TOP SECRET

ZONE 13 FILES ONLY

4

THE MISSING SCIENTISTS

Outside the base, the temperature was minus forty degrees. An icy wind made it feel even colder. People would die in minutes if they were not covered up. This was the Antarctic – the coldest place on Earth.

The base was a small group of huts. In the main hut, it was warm and cosy.

Dr Sue Jones was the head scientist at the base. She looked worried.

'Paul and Terry are late. They haven't radioed in. We had better go and look for them.'

The other scientists agreed. Paul and Terry had gone out to check a weather station. It was only a kilometre away across the ice sheet. They should have been back by now.

Sue and Peter put on their special clothing. Even their faces were covered with special masks. Soon they were roaring over the ice on a power sled. During the Antarctic winter, it was dark even during the day. They used a light to follow the tracks of Paul and Terry's sled. Luckily, the wind hadn't covered the tracks with snow yet.

At last they saw the sled – but there was no sign of Paul and Terry.

BODIES IN THE SNOW

'Look! That's the way they went!'

Peter pointed to the ground. Prints of ice boots led towards a mound of snow. They followed the track.

'It's them!'

Two bodies lay on the ground. The drifting snow was already covering them.

Peter was a doctor. He examined them.

'They're dead. Frozen solid. I can't believe it!'

'What do you mean?'

'They have only been gone two hours. But they're like blocks of ice. A body can't freeze that quickly, not even here!'

Sue went to get the power sled. They would need it to take the bodies back to the base. She was shocked by the death of her friends. Why had they left the sled? How could they have frozen so quickly?

She spotted something in the snow.

'Peter!' she called. 'Come here!'

When Peter reached her, she shone her
torch at the ground.

There were more footprints in the snow. It
looked as if at least six people had been there.
The tracks led away into the distance. The
snow was quickly covering them.

One thing was very clear. No normal person
had made these tracks. No normal person
could walk around in the Antarctic winter in
bare feet ...

3

THE GREY PEOPLE

Sue radioed back to base. The scientists could hardly believe what she said.

'We're going to follow the tracks for a short way,' she said. 'Don't worry – we'll be careful.'

They put the bodies on one of the sleds, then set off. They moved slowly over the snow, following the strange tracks.

'The weather's getting worse,' said Peter. 'We'll have to turn back soon.'

Just then, Sue spotted something. The sled had a powerful light. She shone it at a snow bank.

For just a few seconds, they saw a group of strange figures. Their shape was human, but they were grey in colour. There was a flash of green eyes. Then falling snow hid them from sight.

Both scientists were amazed. Sue wanted to follow them.

'We've got to get back,' said Peter. 'A storm's coming! Two people are dead already!'

Sue knew he was right. She turned the sled around, and they set off back to pick up the bodies of Paul and Terry.

Behind them, the strange grey creatures were standing in a group. They spoke to each other in whispers.

Sue and Peter were well on their way back
to the base. The weather was getting worse.
They went as quickly as they could.

Behind them, the grey people followed their trail through the growing snowstorm.

4

VISITORS AT THE BASE

The other scientists found it difficult to believe the story. How could anything live in this frozen land?

'The falling snow can make your eyes play tricks,' said Jill. Jill was the scientist who was in charge of studying the weather. She was very upset about Paul and Terry. They had been part of her team.

'We didn't just imagine them!' said Peter. 'They were really there!'

Suddenly, the lights went out in the hut! A feeble emergency light flickered on. The hum of the heating system died away.

'The power's gone,' said Sue. 'Why hasn't the back-up generator come on?'

Jamie was in charge of the generators. They were in one of the other buildings. He put on his special clothing.

'I'll go and check them out.'

He left the hut. Minutes later, he was back inside.

'The creatures! The ones you saw! They're right outside!'

They all rushed to the small window. It was difficult to see out. Sue rubbed a clear patch on the glass.

Outside, the grey creatures stood in the snow. There were at least thirty of them.

'Whatever are they?' said Jill. 'Nothing can live out there without special clothes!'

'They've been in the generator building,' said Jamie. 'Both generators are frozen solid.'

'Even if we radio for help, nothing can reach us in this storm,' said Sue. 'But we'll freeze to death if we don't do something.'

The hut had a small store room. Jamie went in and brought out a powerful flame-thrower. It was used in an emergency to melt ice.

'Let's see how they like this!' he said.

SAYING SORRY

Jamie went out of the hut. The grey creatures stood watching him. They didn't make a sound.

Jamie aimed the flame thrower. First, he gave a warning blast, over their heads.

The creatures howled and covered their eyes. They hated the bright light. But they got used to it quickly. One of them came forward. His green eyes stared at Jamie. Before he

could fire, there was a sharp hiss. A white
beam shot from the creature's mouth.

Jamie screamed. Dropping the flame thrower, he staggered back into the hut. Peter tore off Jamie's clothes.

'This arm's frozen solid! I've no choice, Jamie – I'll have to cut it off!'

The hut was freezing now. There was only one chance. Sue put on her special clothing. The others tried to stop her. She wouldn't listen. If they didn't do anything, they would all die anyway.

Outside, the snow was falling faster and faster. It made it very hard to see anything. Sue walked towards the grey creatures. She opened her hands to show she had no weapons.

She pointed to the power sled. The bodies were still on it. One of the grey people walked over to it and looked down. He stared and stared. Then he turned round. He spoke to the others in a strange whisper.

'Any minute now,' thought Sue. 'The icy blast from their mouths that freezes things instantly. At least it will be a quick death!'

But the blast didn't come. The grey people understood at last. They held up their hands. They turned and disappeared into the darkness.

Sue guessed what the sign meant.

They were saying sorry.

An hour later, the generator was running again. The hut was warming up.

'We thought they were dangerous, but they were trying to help us!' said Sue.

'What, by freezing us to death?'

'Wherever they come from, heat is the enemy. They thought we were burning to death! They wanted to save us. If you saw someone on fire, what would you do?'

'Try and put out the fire!'

'That's right. They could feel the heat from the generator. They thought it was killing us!'

In a few months, the short Antarctic summer would come. Where did the strange creatures go then, they wondered? What was their life like?

They were scientists. They knew it was their job to find out.

ABOUT THE AUTHOR

David Orme is an expert on strange, unexplained events. For his protection (and yours) we cannot show a photograph of him.

David created the Zone 13 files to record the cases he studied. Some of these files really do involve aliens, but many do not. Aliens are not everywhere. Just in most places.

These stories are all taken from the Zone 13 files. They will not be here for long. Read them while you can.

But don't close your eyes when you go to sleep at night. **They** will be watching you.